WALT DISNEY PRESENTS

The Bambi Boo

ADAPTED BY
MEL CRAWFORD

ILLUSTRATIONS BY
THE WALT DISNEY STUDIO

gb **GOLDEN PRESS**

**Western Publishing Company, Inc.
Racine, Wisconsin**

© Copyright 1966, 1941 by Walt Disney Productions
World rights reserved. Produced in U.S.A.

GOLDEN, A GOLDEN SHAPE BOOK, and GOLDEN PRESS®
are trademarks of Western Publishing Company, Inc.

Eleventh Printing, 1973

Bambi takes his first steps.

Some of the forest creatures
come to see . . .

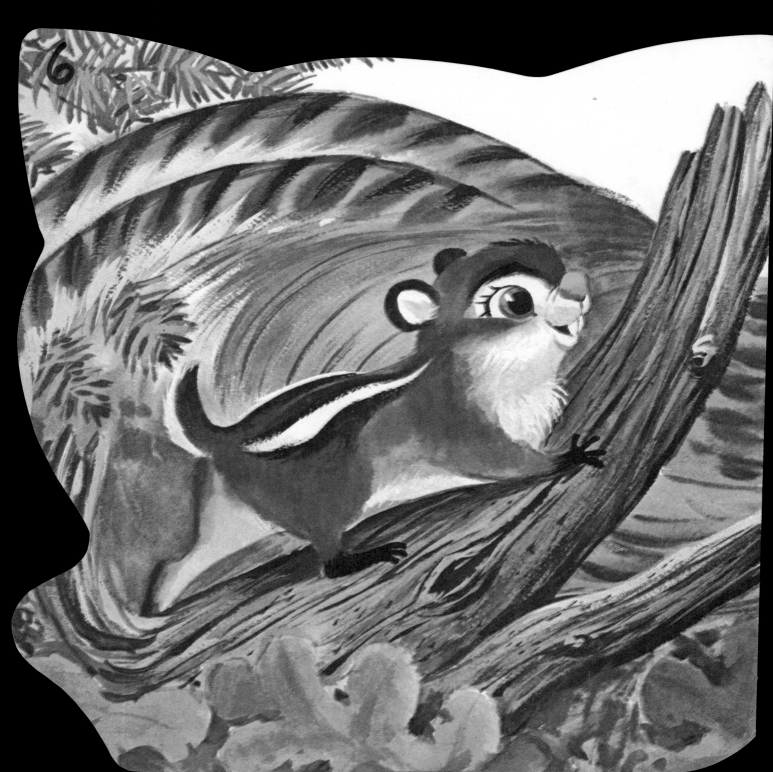

. . . and still more come.

Old Mr. Owl wakes up
and says, "Who, who!"

Thumper the rabbit becomes
Bambi's first friend.

Bambi tries to play
bunny games.

The opossums give Bambi
an upside-down greeting.

Bambi sees himself in the pool.

Bambi meets Flower the skunk.

The squirrels are storing
nuts for winter.

"Hi, Bambi, come and slide!"

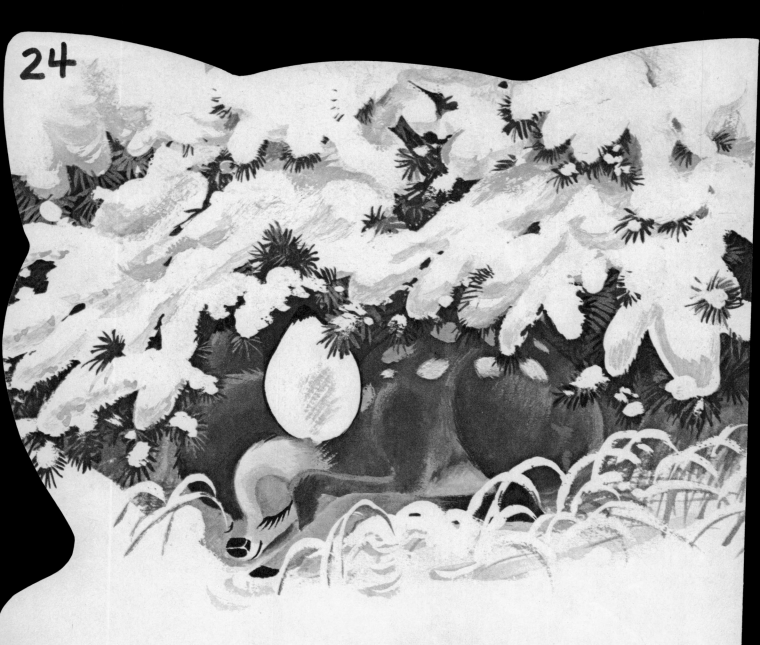

Bambi dreams of spring.